First Published
2022 by Sarah Lou Illustration
Copyright © Sarah Lou 2022

ISBN 978 1 3999 3406 0

Written and illustrated by Sarah Lou
www.sarahlouillustration.co.uk

A CIP catalogue record for this book is available from the British Library.

YOU HAVE A SUPER POWER

For Katie

Buried deep in the wood, a village of people stood.
On the ground and in the air,
sat little houses everywhere.

In one of those houses,
lived Sarah and Katie.
Twin sisters and best friends,
they loved each other greatly.

They would scamper through the trees,
run amongst the meadow flowers,
the grass and the leaves.

Early on one autumn morning, it seemed Katie didn't want to play.
She was very tired and strangely chose to lay in bed all day.

She was really thirsty but she couldn't reach the sink to drink,
her parents were confused, they were not sure what to think.

Dad was worrying and thought it's time to get some
help,
He scooped his daughter up and she let out a tiny yelp.

They zoomed down to the hospital and made it just in
time,
"Katie has type 1 diabetes" revealed the nurse when they
arrived.

"Diet beefies?" Asked Sarah as she looked at dad astonished.
"No, dia-be-tees, silly!" Dad told her as he reached into his pocket.
His hand emerged holding a shiny packet of crisps, POP!

"Oh no!" He cried as they exploded everywhere, they didn't seem to
STOP!
The room erupted loudly into giggles and laughter,
It was the small pick me up they were all after.

The hospital became Katie's second home for a while,
Mum stayed beside her, always with a smile.

Doctors taught her how to manage blood sugar and insulin,
she was fascinated and made sure that she was listening.

While Katie was away, Sarah trudged to school alone.
If Katie was being brave,
then she could do this on her own.

Finally the day had come for Katie to return back home,
She couldn't wait to snuggle in her bed,
and hug her family, never letting go.
School was different now, the other children weren't sure
what to say.
But Katie had Sarah, they only needed each other to play

Eventually it was easier injecting insulin,
managing blood sugars and food.

Katie was the bravest,
she never let it spoil her mood.

A while down the line the brave young lady went to see her nurse,
They called her from the doctors office, it was time they should
converse.
Katie was concerned, she said "I don't like being different!"

But being different is what makes you so magnificent!

Katie looked confused, she slumped upon the bed.
"You should be proud of yourself!" The nurse said, "don't be upset!"

Katie was perplexed, she didn't understand
"Don't you know you have a superpower!?" The nurse exclaimed
waving his hand

"Look at what you overcame! You're so blooming BRAVE!"
A rush of hope washed over Katie, like a wicked tidal WAVE!

Now here's something she never knew
that came as quite a shock,
Guess what?

The nurse had diabetes too,
He wanted to help people "just like me and you!"
Everyone has a superpower,
it's just that some are hard to see,
You can be a hero too, you're born with BRAVERY!

9 781399 934060